THE

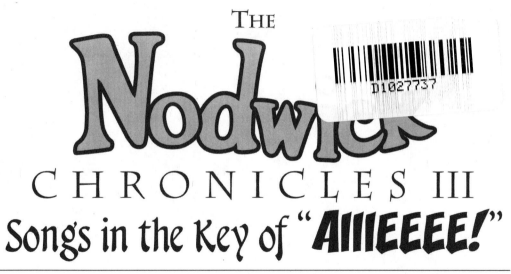

CHRONICLES III
Songs in the Key of "AIIIEEEE!"

A HENCHMAN COLLECTION OF NODWICK 13-18

BY AARON WILLIAMS

**Published by Henchman Publishing,
Distributed by Dork Storm Press**

P.O. Box 10032
Kansas City, MO 64171
E-mail: aaron@nodwick.com

Marketing & Advertising:
sales@dorkstorm.com

**Printed in the United States
First Printing, June 2003
ISBN 1-930964-81-1**

Dedicated to my sister,
Lauren and her child-to-be...

...and her husband, Spencer,
who I hope finds the whole
childbirth thing to be non-icky.

TABLE OF CONTENTS

Everything is funny as long as it is happening to somebody else.

--Will Rogers

If a man does only what is required of him, he is a slave. If a man does more than is required of him, he is a free man.

--Chinese Proverb

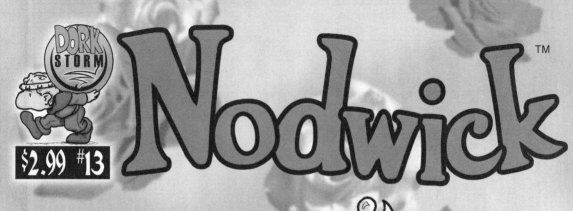

DORK STORM

$2.99 #13

Nodwick ™

chains of LOVE

8

10

11

THE BUCKET ISN'T FOR SALE.

OH, **BUT OF COURSE!** HOW **SILLY** OF ME! I SHALL LOOK ELSEWHERE FOR MY **BUCKET NEEDS!** MERCI, MON AMI AVEC DE CHAPEAU METALLIQUE!

WHAT HE SAID.

I DO HOPE HE WASN'T SHOPPING FOR **HEADGEAR...**

IF YOU WAIT JUST A **MOMENT**, SIR, I'LL HAVE YOUR **LEMONADE** READY!

HERE'S YOUR WATER

THANK YOU! JUST POUR IT INTO THE TUB WITH THE OTHER INGREDIENTS AND I'LL DO THE REST.

13

SMASH!

snap!

tinkle!

MY HEAD FEELS... ALL **GOOEY** AND STUFF...
AND WHY IS NODWICK SO **SCRUMPTIOUSLY HONEY-
CUTE LOOKING** ALL OF A SUDDEN... OOOH, THAT
HEAVENLY-LOOKING **NOSE**, THAT **DARLING** HELMET,
I JUST WANNA **GRAB HIM ALL UP** AND **SMOOCH**—

15

17

18

ER, THERE **WASN'T** ANY WAX, AND THE STOPPER **FELL OUT** WHEN YOU WERE WAVING THE BOTTLE AROUND.

I SHOULD NEVER HAVE LEFT THE HOUSE WITHOUT HAVING MY MORNING CUP OF COFFEE...

WE USED THIS THING TO TAKE OUT THE **TWO-THOUSAND-YEAR-OLD GATES** ON THE **LAIR OF THE FOREST LICH**, SO I DON'T THINK YOU'LL HAVE ANY PROBLEMS USING IT TO LET THE PEOPLE IN THE APARTMENT ABOVE YOU KNOW THEY'RE BEING TOO NOISY.

DID YOU JUST HEAR SOME **SCREAMING**?

WELL, WE JUST MOVED A **LOT** OF MERCHANDISE IN THE MAGIC STUFF AREA, SO WE'VE GOT SPACE IF YOU WANT TO ADD SOME MORE ITEMS.

I DIDN'T KNOW THAT DEMONIC BEINGS HONORED BREAKAGE POLICIES. OF COURSE, I DIDN'T KNOW THEY CARRIED **MONEY**, EITHER...

WELL THAT'S **GREAT**! I'LL HAVE THAT FRANSWA GUY MIND THE STORE AND WE'LL GO RESTOCK THE SHELVES!

19

A FEW HOURS LATER...

WOW, WE'VE REALLY BEEN **MOVING** THE **MERCHANDISE!**

I AM A **TAD CONCERNED** ABOUT THOSE KIDS YOU SOLD SOME OF MY OLD **WANDS** TO. I'M PRETTY SURE SOME OF THEM WERE STILL **CHARGED**, AND I'M **CERTAIN** THAT THE **SMOKE** RISING FROM TWO BLOCKS AWAY **WASN'T** THERE BEFORE

I... HAVE... SOLD... THEM **ALL.**

REALLY? EVERY ONE?

OUI, MONSIEUR. ZEE **CAPITAN** OF ZEE GUARD WAS EENTERESTED IN HAVING YOUR... **USED UNMENTIONABLES**... ZEE NEXT TIME ZEE KING NEEDED TO EMPLOY **CHEMICAL WARFARE** ON ZEE **NEIGHBORING FIEFDOM**.

MERCI. AU REVOIR.

HEY, YOU DROPPED THIS.

KEEP EET. EET HAS CAUSED ME NOTHING BUT TROUBLE.

I ALMOST FORGOT: WHERE DID YOU PUT THE MONEY FROM YOUR SALES?

ZAT **VISION** OF CLERICAL PERFECTION TOOK IT AWAY, MONSIEUR

YOU MEAN **PIFFANY?**

OUI. SHE SEEMED **MOST INSISTANT.**

HERE'S YOUR **RECEIPT, SIR FRITZ BLACKSMITHING** THANKS YOU FOR YOUR PATRONAGE.

HUH?

21

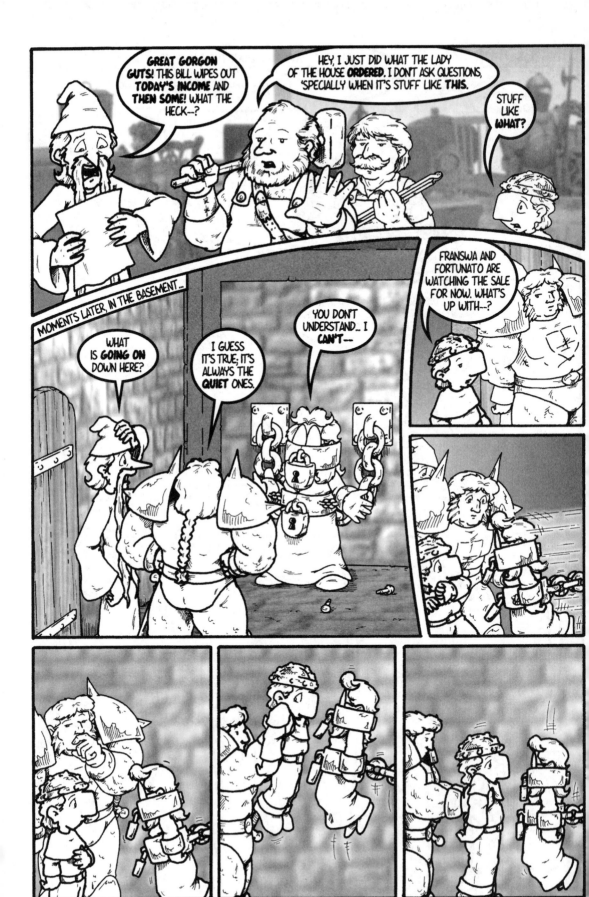

25

WHAT ARE YOU DOING?! I'M STILL--

ARTAX SAID YOU'D BE **FINE**. BESIDES, I THINK THE TOWN GUARD MAY BE IN THE MARKET FOR SOME **USED SHACKLES.**

PIFFANY?

27

YOU **DISARMED** AND **REMOVED** THE TRAPS, AND YOU'RE **FEEDING** THE MONSTERS BY USING THE **TREASURE** THEY'RE SUPPOSED TO BE **GUARDING**. DOES THAT ABOUT COVER IT?

I ALSO... ER... UM...

SPIT IT OUT, PIFFANY. THE **TRUTH** WILL SET YOU **FREE**.

I HUNG CURTAINS....

EXCUSE ME, BUT IF I'M GOING TO DEAL WITH THIS PROBLEM, I NEED TO GO GET **COMPLETELY RIPPED**.

AND I NEED TO GO TO THE LAB. I'LL HAVE TO GET SOME **POTENT SPELLS** TOGETHER TO GET THE SCENT OF **POTPOURRI** OUT OF THIS PLACE...

HOW DID HE KNOW ABOUT THE POTPOURRI?

LUCKY GUESS?

39

41

WE JUST GOT THE FIRST MONTH'S INCOME FROM SELLING HER MORE **PORTABLE** PIECES. I'M TOLD THAT A FEW OF THEM ARE ON DISPLAY IN MORE THAN ONE **ROYAL RESIDENCE.**

ARE **ALL** OF THE CREATURES LIVING HERE THIS... **TALENTED?**

NOT QUITE, BUT EVERYONE CONTRIBUTES. WHEN PIFFANY GAVE US A TASTE OF HOW LIFE COULD BE WITHOUT **KILLING** EVERYTHING THAT MOVES, WE DISCOVERED MORE **POSITIVE** OUTLETS FOR OUR STRENGTHS AND ABILITIES.

AH. WELL, THERIN LIES THE **PROBLEM.** WE HAD A TALK WITH OUT **REAL ESTATE AGENT,** AND—

--AND WE COULDN'T BE **HAPPIER** WITH WHAT YOU'VE DONE WITH THE PLACE! TELL YOU WHAT, I SAW SOME LOVELY **PINECONES** AND **WILDFLOWERS** THAT WOULD MAKE A KEEN **CENTERPIECE,** AND I NEED TO GATHER THEM BEFORE NIGHT FALLS.

I UNDERSTAND. WE TOO HAVE DISCOVERED THE **JOYS** OF THE **HUMBLE PINECONE.** THANK YOU AGAIN FOR ALL OF YOUR HELP!

I CAN'T DO IT, NODWICK.

OH, I DON'T KNOW. WHY WAIT FOR **FALL** IF YOU WANT PINECONE CENTERPIECES?

NO, I CAN'T MAKE THEM **EVIL** AGAIN! THEY USED TO BE **STINKY BAD-NAUGHTIES** AND NOW THEY'RE **ARTISTS** AND **FARMERS** AND STUFF!

WELL, MAYBE WE SHOULD GO LOOK AT THE **OTHER** PLACES WE'RE BEING MEASURED AGAINST. PERHAPS THEY AREN'T AS **BAD** AS DYBBUK MAKES THEM OUT TO BE.

45

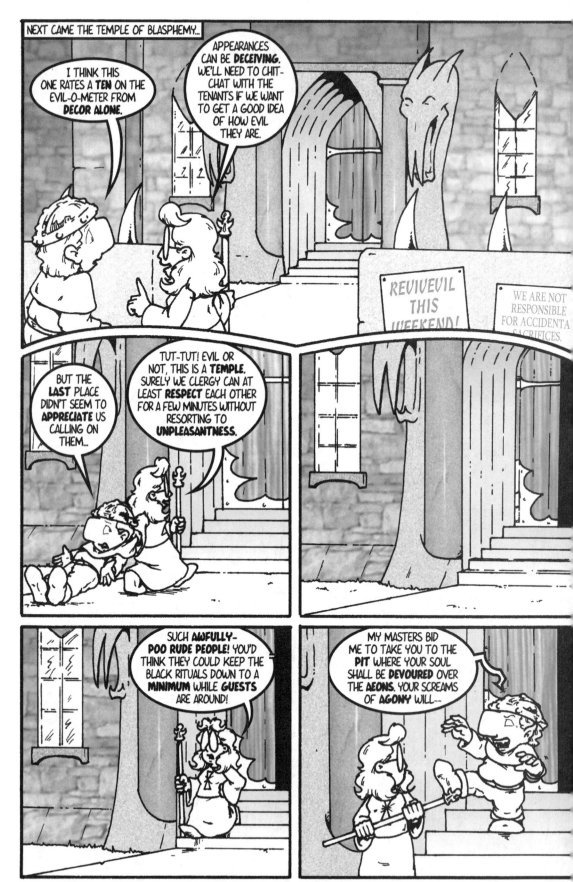

YOU'VE HEARD OF THE **HOLLOW OF HAZARDOUS HORROR?** THAT'S US. WE WERE IN THE MIDDLE OF **REMODELING** AND WE THOUGHT TO OURSELVES, "WHY, WHO WILL WE EVER GO TO IF WE NEED TO BORROW A CUP OF **SUGAR?**"

WE HAVE **NO SUGAR** HERE. ALL WE HAVE IS THE SWEET TASTE OF **DESPAI—**

SO TO MAKE SURE WE START THINGS OFF ON THE **RIGHT FOOT,** I BROUGHT ALONG SOME **MONK-MUNCHIES** AND **SISTER-SCOUT COOKIES!**

ARE ANY OF THESE THE CHOCOLATE MINT ONES?

WOW! WE MADE IT OUT **ALIVE!** THOSE GUYS WEREN'T SO **BAD,** I GUESS...

OH, NO! THEY WERE **MASSIVELY EVIL!**

DIDN'T YOU NOTICE HOW THEY DRANK **WATER** WITH THEIR COOKIES RATHER THAN **MILK?** IF EVER THERE WAS A **GREATER** SIGN OF **COMPLETE AND TOTAL CORRUPTION,** I DON'T WANT TO KNOW WHAT IT IS!

ON TO THE **NEXT** DEN OF NAUGHTINESS!

WAIT, SO THREATENING TO FEED US TO AN **ABYSSAL LURKER** ISN'T AS GREAT A CHARACTER FLAW AS CHOOSING THE **WRONG BEVERAGE?**

HOURS LATER, BACK AT THE HOLLOW...

WELL **THAT** DIDN'T WORK, EITHER.

OKAY, **GOLEMS** AREN'T MY **STRONG SUIT.** BESIDES, I DIDN'T THINK THEY'D MAKE THEM INTO **GARDEN ACCESSORIES...**

BESIDES, YOUR **"EVIL LESSONS"** MADE THINGS WORSE. NOW THEY JUST CHANNEL THEIR "NEGATIVITY" INTO MORE "CREATIVE OUTLETS."

OH? AND YOUR **MAGIC WARDS** FIXED EVERYTHING, DIDN'T THEY?

HEY, IF I WAS **GOOD** AT LAYING DOWN MAGICAL TRAPS, I WOULDN'T BE SHARING A MORTGAGE WITH **YOU.**

OH, YEAH, YOU'D BE IN AN IMPENETRABLE **MAGIC FORTRESS** SURROUNDED BY AN **ARMY OF GOLEMS,** RIGHT?

DON'T MAKE ME BRING UP YOUR **"BETTER EVIL THROUGH BEER"** SCHEME...

WELL I HAD **FUN** WITH THAT ONE, AT LEAST...

ARE WE THERE YET?

I THINK SO.

OH, GOOD. SHALL WE?

LET'S.

SPLAT!

51

55

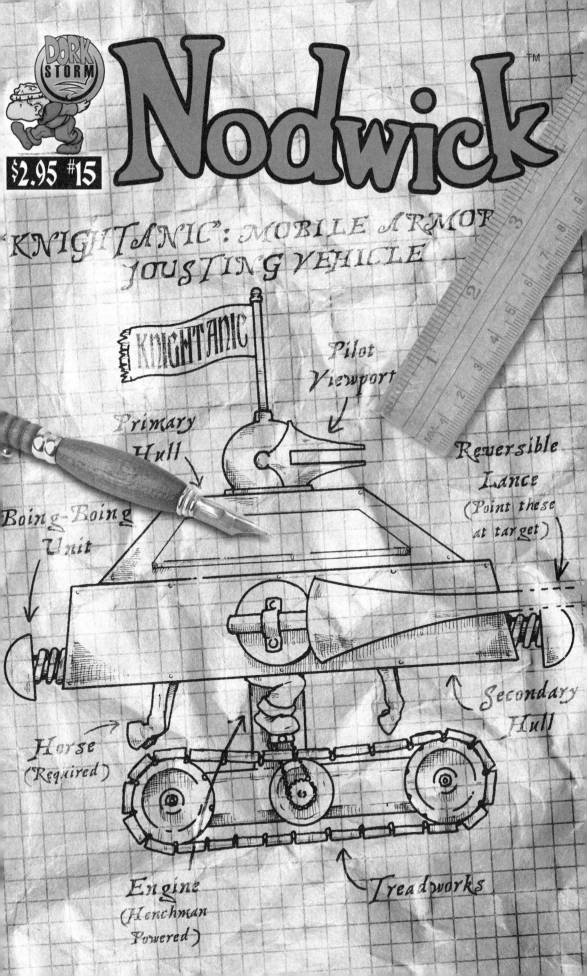

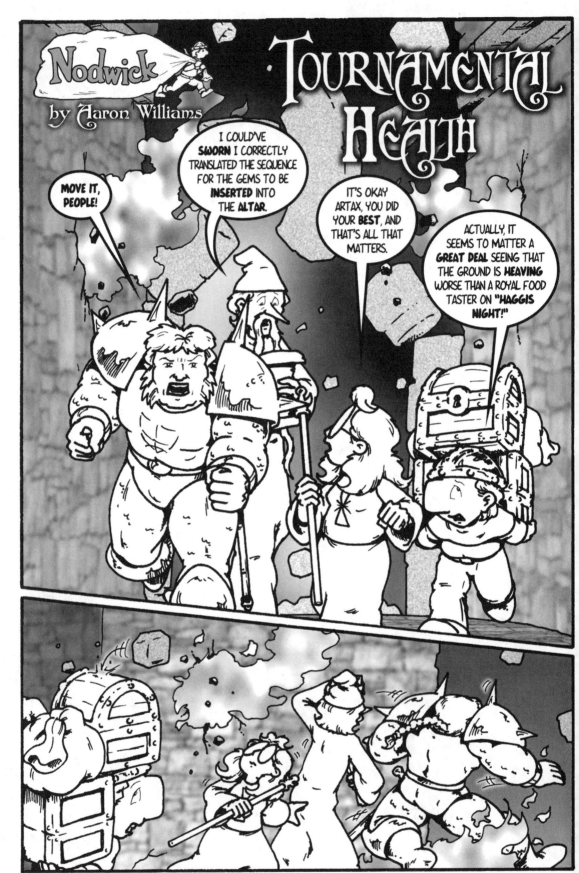

POIT!

WELL, AT LEAST THAT **EVIL-STINKY TEMPLE** IS GONE FOR ANOTHER HUNDRED YEARS.

BUT IF I HADN'T MESSED UP, WE WOULD'VE BEEN ABLE TO RETRIEVE THE **ROD OF MOEBEOS**, AMONG OTHER VALUABLE STUFF. INSTEAD, WE LOST THAT ALONG WITH THE CHANCE TO **PERMANENTLY** DESTROY THE TEMPLE.

OH, IT'S NOT YOUR FAULT.

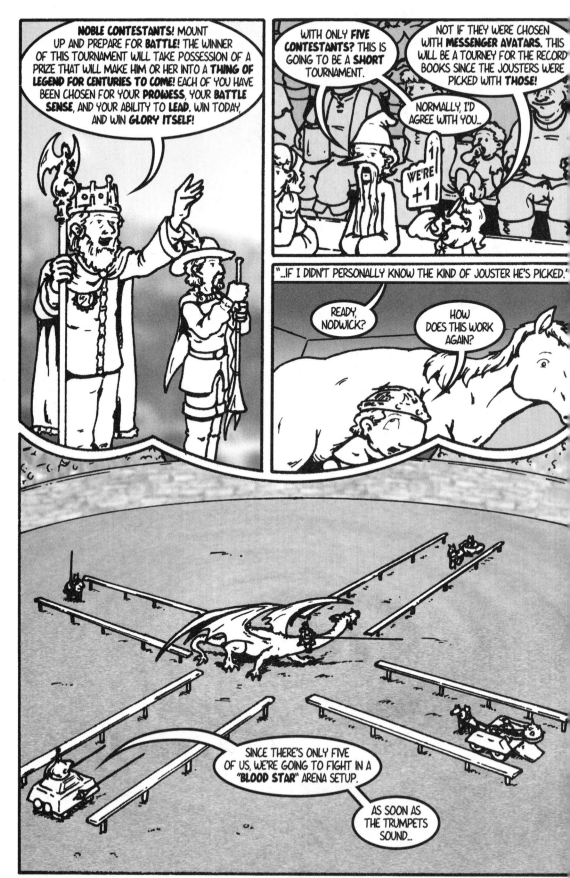

70

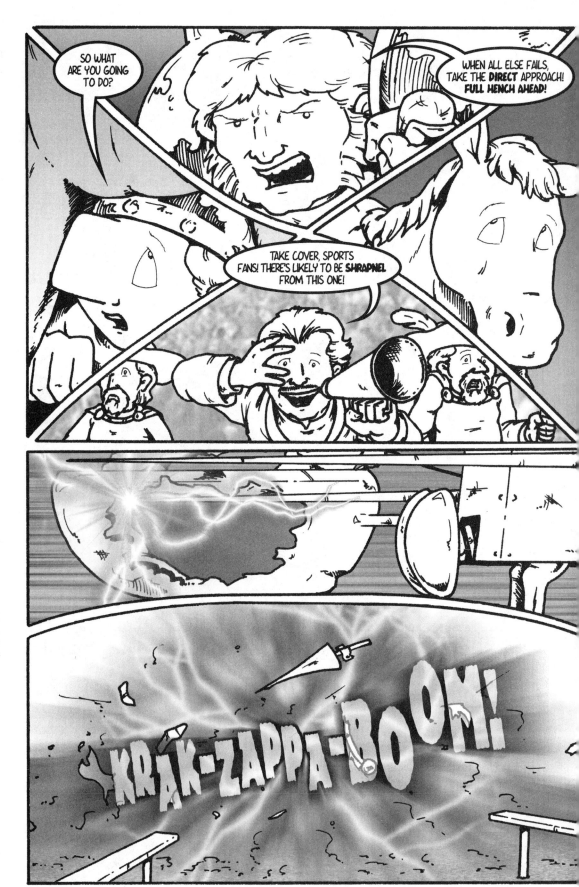

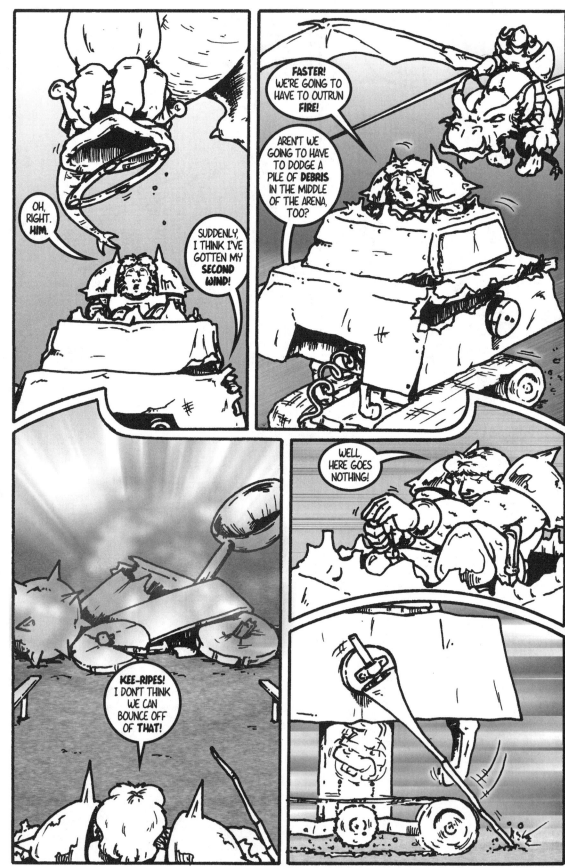

74

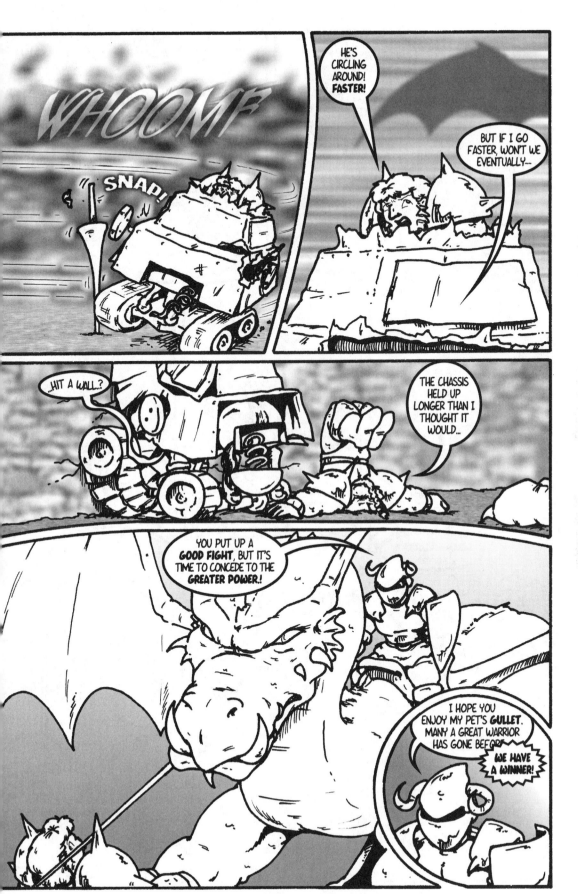

Nodwick

BY AARON WILLIAMS

RUNNING *the* GAUNTLET

FROM ARTAX'S JOURNAL: IT HAS BEEN AN ODD FEW MONTHS SINCE YEAGAR WON THE TOURNAMENT AND GAINED HIS **MAGICAL GAUNTLET.** FOR ONE, WE DIDN'T REALIZE THAT A **KINGDOM** CAME WITH IT.

NOT THAT HE WOULD HAVE **NEEDED** TO BE CROWNED, MIND YOU. AFTER ALL, HE DOES HAVE THE **GAUNTLET** AND ALL THE **POWERS** THAT COME WITH IT...

THE GAUNTLET IS AN **IMPRESSIVE** ARTIFACT. NO BLOW CAN LAND ON YEAGAR WHILE HE WEARS IT, AND HE CAN SEND **ELDRITCH ENERGIES** FROM IT WITH **DEVASTATING EFFECT.**

FOR STARTERS, NO ONE CAN DISOBEY HIS EVERY WHIM WHEN HE'S AROUND. HE APPOINTED ME **'COURT MAGICIAN,'** AND I CAN'T TELL IF I ACCEPTED BECAUSE I **WANTED** TO OR IF THE GAUNTLET **COMPELLED** ME TO.

PIFFANY HAS MADE HERSELF THE **LIAISON** FROM HER **CLERICAL ORDER** TO HIS COURT, AND HE DOESN'T SEEM TO MIND.

NODWICK HAS BEEN KEPT BUSY REARRANGING THE ROYAL FURNITURE AND CLEARING SPACE FOR THE **LARGEST DISTILLERY** IN THE KINGDOM.

I WRITE THESE WORDS SO THAT I MIGHT HAVE A RECORD OF MY THOUGHTS WHEN **NOT** UNDER KING YEAGAR'S **INFLUENCE.** I'VE SCOURED THE ROYAL LIBRARIES, AND I'VE DISCOVERED SOME **DISTURBING THINGS** ABOUT THE METAL GLOVE HE WEARS.

I ONLY HOPE I CAN **ACT** ON THIS KNOWLEDGE BEFORE I'M 'CONVINCED' TO DO **OTHERWISE**--

HEY, ART! WHAT'S SHAKING?

OH! UM, NOT MUCH, YOUR MAJESTY.

HAH, FORGET THAT "YOUR MAJESTY" STUFF. WHAT'RE YOU LOOKING UP?

MAGICAL ARTIFACTS...

TO BE SPECIFIC, YOUR **GAUNTLET**--

YEAH, ISN'T IT **GREAT?** I THINK I'VE LEARNED ENOUGH ABOUT IT TO EFFECTIVELY LEAD MY **ARMY.**

ARMY? **WHAT** ARMY?

OH, THE **ANSERINIAN EMPIRE** IS CAUSING TROUBLE ON THE BORDER.

I'M GOING TO LEAD AN **EXPEDITIONARY FORCE** TO THE BORDER ZONE AND MAKE SURE THEY KNOW WE WON'T PUT UP WITH ANY **SHENANIGANS.**

I MUST SAY, **BEING KING** SEEMS TO AGREE WITH YOU.

NO JOKE! I DON'T KNOW IF IT'S THE **GLOVE** OR NOT, BUT I'VE NEVER FELT MORE **CONFIDENT!** I FEEL LIKE I COULD TAKE ON THE **WORLD!**

WELL, I GOTTA GO **REST UP** FOR TOMORROW. I'LL LEAVE YOU IN CHARGE WHILE I'M GONE, NATCH. JUST BE SURE NO ONE GETS IN MY **WINE CELLAR.**

YOU GOT IT.

89

96

NODWICK DIDN'T NEED TO FEEL SORRY FOR LONG...

OH, **THAT** WASN'T **NICE** AT **ALL!** I GOT IN **SO MUCH** TROUBLE!

BROTHERHOOD OF EVIL HENCHM DIRECTORY

THEOGOR TOLD ME THAT IF I DIDN'T COME BACK WITH YOU IN **TWENTY MINUTES**, I'D BE **SMART** TO **NOT** COME BACK AT ALL!

THEN YOU DON'T HAVE TO GO BACK. I THINK I LAST SAW YOU ABOUT **THIRTY** MINUTES AGO.

OH, YOU'RE RIGHT. I KNEW I SHOULDN'T HAVE STOPPED IN THE BATHROOM TO **MOISTEN** MY BRAIN!

TOUGH BREAK. YOU WIN SOME, YOU LOSE SOME.

SIGH... TOO TRUE.

YOU SHOULD LEARN TO **RELAX.** IF YOU NEED ME, YOU'LL KNOW WHERE TO FIND ME.

ONE SCRUBBING LATER...

BÂTH

I'M GOING TO HAVE TO PICK MY WORDS MORE **CAREFULLY,** AREN'T I?

I THINK HE DID IT TO US AGAIN...

NO, NOT... WAIT...

WHISPERING?

I THINK IT'S COMING FROM THE STAGE.

I HAVE AN **EAVESDROPPING SPELL** THAT MIGHT LET US LISTEN IN.

GATHER AROUND...

...AND YOU'LL HAVE **POWER** AND **RICHES**. WOMEN WILL **THROW** THEMSELVES AT YOUR **FEET**. ROYALTY THAT HAS ENDURED FOR **GENERATIONS** WILL **BOW** TO YOU.

WHAT DO I DO?

CRUSH YOUR ENEMIES. **OVERTHROW** YOUR OPPONENTS.

WELL, IF ONE IS GOING TO GO **MAD**, I SUPPOSE IT HELPS TO HAVE SOMEONE STRAPPING ROLLER SKATES TO YOUR FEET AND GIVING YOU A PRETTY GOOD **PUSH**.

WHO ARE MY ENEMIES?

EVERYONE WHO **DOESN'T** SUBMIT TO YOUR WILL IS AN **ENEMY**.

EVERYONE?

EVERYONE, BE THEY A **COUNTRY** OR A MERE **SERVANT**. NO ONE SHOULD DISOBEY YOU.

OH, COOKIE CRUMBS...

LOOK AT THE AUDIENCE. NOTICE ANYTHING **STRANGE**?

MY COUNSEL IS THE **WISEST**. LISTEN TO **ME**, AND YOUR ACTIONS WILL NEVER BE WRONG.

NO ONE SHOULD DISOBEY ME.

I WILL NEVER BE WRONG.

NOW, WHAT WILL YOU DO?

I WILL CRUSH MY ENEMIES.

SHOW THEM NO MERCY.

SHOW NO MERCY.

WHAT DOES IT MEAN?

I'M NOT SURE, BUT I KNOW WE DON'T HAVE A LOT OF **TIME**. LET'S MOVE ON.

110

ALL ACROSS YEAGAR'S MINDSCAPE...

...ROWEN AFTER ROWEN...

...LETS HER PAIN SPRING FORTH...

...AND COMFORT IS PROVIDED.

WHO IS THIS "ROWEN" PERSON? AND WHY--?

LESS **CONJECTURE**, MORE **SNEAKING**. INVISIBLE CASTLE, REMEMBER?

SUDDENLY, BACK IN THE "REAL WORLD..."

WRONG. THIS IS **WRONG**...

M'LORD?

WHAT AM I **DOING**? I'M GOING TO GO KILL **HUNDREDS** OF PEO--

POWER.

WEALTH.

RESPECT.

GLORY...

113

115

119

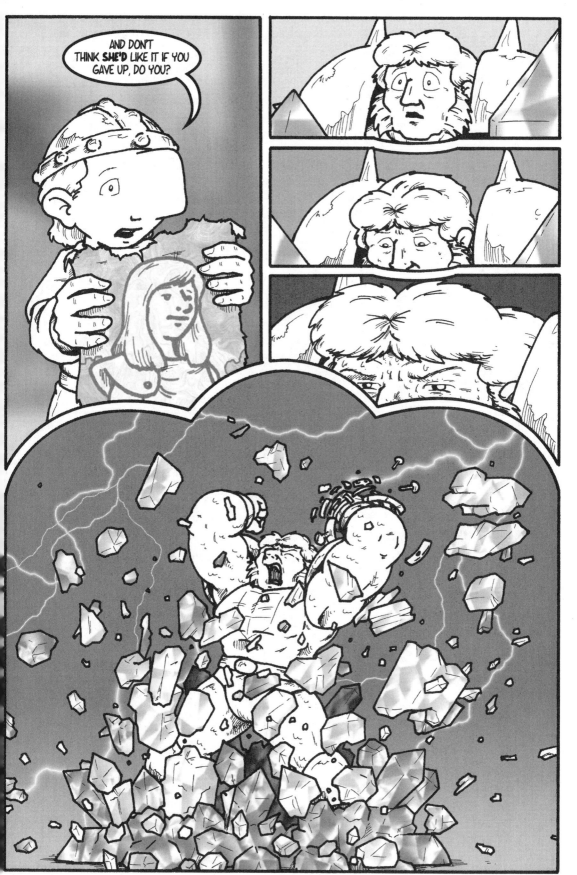

123

125

$2.99 #18

130

Once upon a time, a poor wood-carver wished for a son. He was old and had no wife, and no one to inherit his shop or learn his trade. So, one day, he decided to make a son from a fine piece of wood he found in the forest. He carved with great skill and painted the puppet with a steady hand, but for all his efforts, it remained mere wood....

AH, BUT IF ONLY YOU WERE A **REAL** BOY, MY PINOCCHIO. AH, WELL, I SUPPOSE **ADOPTION** WOULD HAVE MADE MORE SENSE AFTER ALL...

I WISH... I WISH...

I WISH I'D GONE INTO **REAL ESTATE** LIKE MY BROTHER. **CARPENTRY** IS FOR THE **BIRDS**.

CHIRP! CHIRP!

STOMP!

AND I CAN'T KEEP THE FRIGGIN' **CRICKETS** OUT OF MY HOUSE...

133

Once upon yet another time, a poor fool traded his mother's cow for magic beans. Upon planting them, they grew into a beanstalk that reached up, up, and into the clouds! Being not afraid, the fool boldly climbed into the sky to see what the beanstalk held in store. He made it to the top of the beanstalk, and beheld a castle, floating upon the clouds!

AMAZING! SUCH A **WONDER!**

THAT A CASTLE, **TEN TIMES AS LARGE** AS ANY I HAVE SEEN, COULD BE **SUPPORTED** BY THE CLOUDS!

HOW CAN THIS **BE?**

HEY. HOW **CAN** THIS BE? AND THAT BY **SHEER COINCIDENCE**, A BEANSTALK PLANTED IN A **RANDOM FARM** WOULD LEAD STRAIGHT TO IT...

And then the fool remembered he was SUPPOSED to be a fool, and got on with it!

ZONK!

UH, DUHHHHHH... **PRETTY CASTLE...**

The fool made his way into the castle

OH, YOU MUST **HELP ME!**

HUH?

THE LORD OF THIS CASTLE IS A **NAUGHTY-ICK GIANT**, AND I, A **MAGIC HARP**, AM HIS PRISONER, MADE TO PLAY THE MOST **BAWDY** AND **NOT-NICE SONGS** ABOUT DRINKING AND PINCHING PEOPLE, AND ALL SORTS OF DIRTY-POO THINGS.

BUT WHAT CAN **I** DO, FOR I AM BUT A **POOR FOOL?**

YOU MUST RESCUE **ME** AND THE **GOOSE** THAT LAYS **GOLDEN EGGS.**

THE GOOSE THAT DOES **WHAT?**

LAYS GOLDEN EGGS.

WHAT THE HECK ARE YOU **FEEDING** IT?

FEE-FIE-FO-FUM! I SMELL THE NOSE OF A SMALL HENCHMAN!

A HENCH *WHAT?*

I DON'T KNOW. IT JUST POPPED INTO MY HEAD.

SPEAKING OF **POPPING**, THAT NOISE RESEMBLING A STARVING MAN CHOWING DOWN ON CELERY IS MY **SPINE**...

*O*nce upon a time, a beautiful princess was under the spell of an evil witch, and she was made to sleep for a hundred years. One day, a handsome prince rode up on a horse. All he needed to do was bestow a kiss upon--

NOT ON YOUR LIFE.

AND WE'VE BOTH DONE THE **WITCH** AND **PRINCE** THING ALREADY.

*O*nce upon a time, there was a little girl named Goldilocks. She was wandering the forest, when she came upon the home of the three bears. Being hungry, she smelled the porridge cooling in the house, and--

BUT I'M STILL FULL FROM EATING THE GINGERBREAD HOUSE.

Da

Once upon a time, a little girl in a Red Riding hood was sent with a basket of goodies to take to her grandmother. There was a deep, dark forest between Red Riding hood and her Grandmother's house, and in it, lived a big, bad wolf.

Once upon a time, there was a beautiful princess. Her beauty was so great it outshone that of the queen. The queen grew jealous, and exiled the princess to the forest, in the hopes that she would be felled by the beasts living there. The princess was found by a kindly troupe of seven dwarves, five of whom were on vacation, and one of which had a hyperactive thyroid condition...

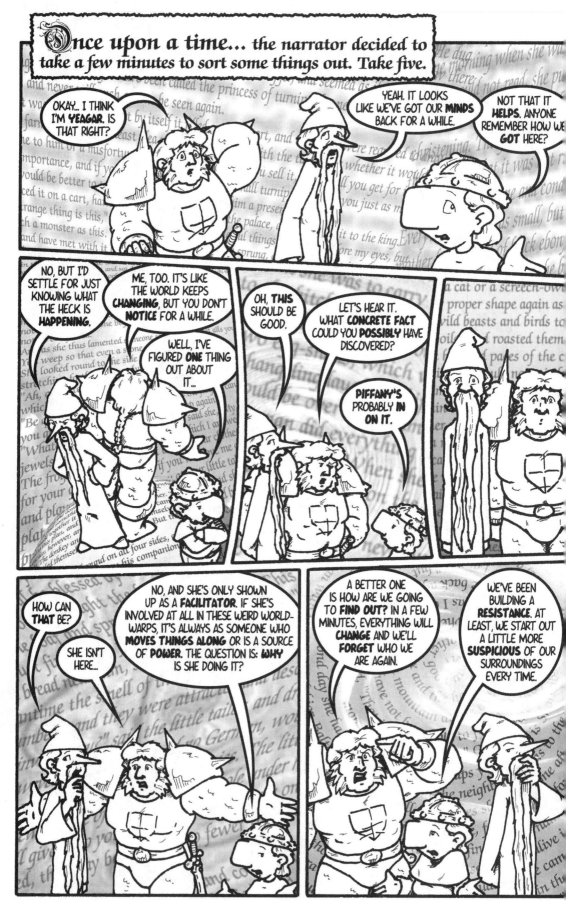

144

The Henchman

A New Core Class for the d20 System • by Chris Pramas

All information after the "Game Rule Information" heading is designated as Open Game Content

Henchmen are a common sight in dungeons everywhere. No self-respecting adventuring party would delve into the depths without a henchman along. Someone's got to carry all that treasure above ground after all, and it's not going to be the holier-than-thou paladin or the effete wizard. Adventuring parties treat henchmen like pieces of equipment, no more or less important than 50 feet of silk rope or a 10 foot pole. The exploits of henchmen are largely unsung, as big nosed midgets are not the bards' hero of choice.

Hard work, low pay, and frequent death— those are the realities of the henchman's life.

Adventures:

Henchmen have no trouble at all finding adventures. If anything, their lives are too eventful, as overconfident adventuring parties drag them into killer dungeons, volcanic lairs, and vortexes of madness.

Characteristics: The henchman is the workhorse of the adventuring party. It is his job to carry all the loot, act as live monster bait, and trigger traps that can't be disarmed. For all these services and more, he gets only the payment stipulated in his contract. If the party scores big, the henchman doesn't see even one extra gold piece. And glory? Forget about it.

Alignment: Henchmen are neutral of good alignments. While there may be evil henchmen, they are members of a different union or independent operators and they have abilities that reflect their wicked natures.

Religion: Henchmen honor the ancestor spirit of the very first henchman, known as the Alpha Lugger, the Great Mover, and the Supreme Seneschal. Other than that worship is fairly individual. One curious side effect of henchmen's ability to come back from the dead over and over again (see below) is that they often form friendly relationships with certain gods and celestials.

Background: Henchmen are a curious subset of the working class. They have their own union but it works to their detriment as often as it helps them. For the population at large, henchmen are useful tools but nothing more. Most folks have more tender feelings for their favorite horse than their henchman.

Races: Members of any humanoid race can become henchmen, but all eventually take on the "hench form" (see below).

Other Classes: Henchmen have the same relationship with all other classes: servitude.

Game Rule Information

Henchmen have the following game statistics.

Abilities: Since henchmen take so much abuse, a high Constitution is a great boon. A good Strength helps in carrying the party's treasure back home.

Alignment: Lawful Good, Neutral Good, Chaotic Good, Lawful Neutral, Neutral, and Chaotic Neutral.

Hit Die: d12

Class Skills

The henchman's class skills (and the key ability for each skill) are: Appraise (Int), Balance (Dex), Bluff (Cha), Climb (Str), Escape Artist (Dex), Gather Information (Cha), Handle Animal (Cha), Hide (Dex), Jump (Str), Listen (Wis), Search (Int), Spot (Wis), Swim (Str), and Use Rope (Dex).

Skill Points at 1st Level: (4 + Int modifier) x 4.

Skill Points at Each Additional Level: 4 + Int modifier.

Class Features

Armor and Weapon Proficiency: Henchmen are proficient with all simple weapons. They are not proficient in any type of armor, nor with shields. Most henchmen do wear helmets, but these offer very little in the way of protection.

A henchman's helm does not increase Armor Class, but it does offer a small chance to avoid critical hits. Whenever a henchman suffers a critical hit, roll a d20. On a roll of 20, the helm catches the blow and the critical hit is negated. Normal damage is still inflicted.

Become Irrelevant (Ex): Henchmen are, quite literally, beneath the notice of most creatures. A henchman can stand in plain sight and others will talk about him as if he isn't there. This can be useful in many circumstances. A henchman (and only a henchman) can use his Hide skill to "become irrelevant." The henchman makes a Hide check opposed by Spot checks from anyone observing the henchman at the time. A successful Hide check means the henchman has become irrelevant and can act as if invisible for the next 1d4 rounds.

Damage Soak (Ex): In times of crisis, adventurers often treat their henchmen as living shields. An adventurer can assign the damage suffered from a single attack or spell to a nearby henchman. The henchman, who must be within 10 feet of the adventurer, can soak a number of hit points equal to his level x 3 (see Table 1). Damage in excess of the henchman's damage soak is suffered by the adventurer as normal.

For example, Edwyg the wizard takes a critical hit from a frenzied orc. The wizard would normally take 23 points of damage, killing him. However, since he has a 4th level henchman along, he can reduce this damage by 12. Edwyg suffers 11 points of damage and the henchman 12.

Lug (Ex): The hench-man's primary power is his amazing ability to lug loot

Level	Base Attack Bonus	Fort Save	Ref Save	Will Save	Damage Soak	Lug	Special
1	+0	+2	+0	+0	3	+5	Become Irrelevant, Union Man, Monster Bait
2	+1	+3	+0	+0	6	+10	State the Obvious
3	+1	+3	+1	+1	9	+15	Hench Form
4	+2	+4	+1	+1	12	+20	
5	+2	+4	+1	+1	15	+25	Sweet Death Denied (no Con loss)
6	+3	+5	+2	+2	18	+30	
7	+3	+5	+2	+2	21	+35	Hench Spirit
8	+4	+6	+2	+2	24	+40	
9	+4	+6	+3	+3	27	+45	
10	+5	+7	+3	+3	30	+50	Sweet Death Denied (no level loss)
11	+5	+7	+3	+3	33	+55	
12	+6/+1	+8	+4	+4	36	+60	
13	+6/+1	+8	+4	+4	39	+65	
14	+7/+2	+9	+4	+4	42	+70	
15	+7/+2	+9	+5	+5	45	+75	
16	+8/+3	+10	+5	+5	48	+80	
17	+8/+3	+10	+5	+5	51	+85	
18	+9/+4	+11	+6	+6	54	+90	
19	+9/+4	+11	+6	+6	57	+95	
20	+10/+5	+12	+6	+6	60	+100	

out of dungeons. Such is their ability to pack and stack that a henchman can haul weight far in excess of what his size and strength would suggest. The more experienced the hench-man, the more he can lug. For the purposes of carrying capacity only, a henchman's strength is considered to be (5 x level) greater than it actually is. A 4th level henchman, for example, receives a +20 bonus to his strength when determining carrying capacity.

Monster Bait (Ex): Maybe monsters can't resist a morsel-sized bite, or maybe henchmen just taste extra-delicious, but whatever the reason monster just can't seem to resist them. In combat, monsters will always choose to attack a henchman, all other things being equal. This often gives adventuring parties valuable time to prepare spells or perform "tactical withdrawals."

Union Man: All henchmen must belong to the Henchman's Union, an organization tightly controlled by the Adventurers' Guild. Henchmen are subject to the rules of the union, which have a nasty habit of changing arbitrarily. Such are the strictures of the Henchman's Union that henchmen may never multiclass. When you're a hench, you're a hench all the way, from your first mortal blow to your last dying day.

State the Obvious (Ex): Sometimes adventurers just don't get it. All the clues are there, staring them in the face, but they can't see what's going on. They'd rather try to find Zelda the Leper's cousin (twice removed) in the kingdom's capital, or search the local whorehouse for "clues." When the Gamemaster feels the players are totally off track, he can speak through the henchman (or pass the henchman's player a note) and get the adventurers going in the right direction.

Hench Form (Ex): Henchmen tend to have a very similar physical appearance: short and big of schnoz. While many people think henchmen are a race unto themselves, this

actually isn't the case. Members of any humanoid race can become henchmen, but the job transforms them physically. Their bodies are crushed under the enormous weights they must carry, and their noses get larger to act a counter balance.

By 3rd level, a henchman achieves his "hench form". His height becomes 3 feet plus 1d12 inches and his size becomes Small. As a Small creature, a henchman gains a +1 size bonus to AC, a +1 size bonus to attack rolls, and a + size bonus on Hide checks, but must use smaller weapons than humans. Unlike other Small creatures, henchman suffer no reduction to their carrying capacity.

Henchmen that begin play shorter than their hench form (halflings, for instance) grow rather than shrink. In this case, they have bulked out to better manage their loads.

Sweet Death Denied (Su): Due to the damage soak ability and the general abuse of the hench life, henchmen die and are brought back to life at a terrific rate. Such is the severity of their contracts that even the release of death is denied to them. Interestingly enough, so much positive energy flows throw the broken and mutilated bodies of henchmen that they can be raised from the dead more easily than other creatures. Starting at 5th level, a henchman does not lose any Constitution when brought back with raise dead or resurrection spell. A henchman o

10th level or greater no longer loses a level when brought back with a raise dead spell.

Hench Spirit (Su): Henchmen of 7th level and above are so dedicated to their work (or their contracts are so draconian) that even after they are slain, their spirits remain in the area trying to help their employers (usually by gathering information). Unlike a vengeful ghost, hench spirits have no spooky powers. Their stats remain the same, but they are ethereal (see Condition Summary in Core Rulebook II). A hench spirit remains on the Material Plane for 1d4 days and then dissipates. If it takes even one point of damage during that time, it also dissipates. Henchmen can be raised from the dead or resurrected while a hench spirit or any time thereafter (within the normal limits of spell used).

Ex-Henchmen

There are no ex-Henchmen except the dead. As previously noted, henchmen may never multiclass.

Human Henchman Starting Package

Armor: Helm, speed 30 ft.
Weapons: Dagger (1d4, 19-20/x2, 10 ft., 1 lb., Tiny, Piercing).
Skill Selection: Pick a number of skills equal to 5 + Int modifier.

Skill	Ranks	Ability
Hide	4	Dex
Balance	4	Dex
Spot	4	Wis
Gather Information	4	Cha
Bluff	4	Cha
Climb	4	Str
Handle Animal	4	Cha
Escape Artist	4	Dex
Search	4	Int

Feat: Endurance
Bonus Feat: Toughness
Gear: Backpack with waterskin, one day's trail ration, bedroll, sack, crowbar, and flint and steel.
Gold: 1d4 gp

New Feats

Presented here are two new feats, designed with the employer in mind. Henchmen cannot take these feats, only adventurers of other classes.

Hench Hurling

You can throw your henchman like a javelin. A big nosed, non-aerodynamic javelin...
Prerequisites: Str 13+, Point Blank Shot
Benefit: You can hurl a henchman. If the henchman is unwilling, you must first win a grapple check to ready the "weapon." A henchman has a 10 ft. range increment and inflicts 1d8 damage if helmeted and 1d6 damage if bare headed.
Special: The henchman can act as a living grappling hook if a rope is tied to him. The henchman must make a successful Climb or Str check (DC 15) to grab on to the target wall or outcrop.

Motivator

You can get your henchman to do nearly anything, no matter how suicidal it seems.
Prerequisites: Cha 13+, Bluff 5+ ranks
Benefit: You can make a henchman in your employ follow your orders to the letter by playing on his sense of duty or invoking the fine print in his contract. The henchman must do exactly as ordered, unless he makes a Will save (DC 18 + your Cha modifier).

CREDITS:

AUTHOR: Chris Pramas is the founder and president of Green Ronin Publishing, which has been in d20 game from day one. In his nearly ten years in the gaming industry, he has written for over a dozen RP as both freelancer and staffer. He is best known for the AD&D Guide to Hell and his Origins Award winn Death in Freeport and the Chainmail Miniatures Game. He is reputed to enjoy punk rock and sweet ir

ILLUSTRATOR: Aaron Williams is the creator and illustrator of Nodwick. He also likes goldfish as ʃ

ACKNOWLEDGMENTS

Of course, I'm obligated to thank first and foremost, my wonderful wife, Cristi (it was included in our vows)! Thanks again to those at Dungeon and Dragon Magazines for giving Nodwick a home. Big gratitudes to everyone in the on-line fan club which seems to be growing at a geometric rate, and thanks to everyone who e-mails me about the mistakes I make weekly on the website (fixing the date is a BIG one. I must have a mental block for dates... which really bodes ill for my anniversary). Without them, links would be dead, cartoons would be missing, and visitors would think that it really was still February 2, 1998. Many greetings to the Jolly Roger Games crew for putting out Nodwick's first card game! And last, but not least, the guys at Adventure Retail and "The Source" in St. Paul; Nodwick has a secure destiny thanks to you guys... and that restaurant next door. Try the "Chocolate Monkey." You'll love it.

Aaron

WAR TODAY! PLEASE FORM LINE HERE.

ABOUT THE AUTHOR

At the tender age of ten, Aaron Williams was exposed to Dungeons & Dragons, and his Charles Shultz-inspired drawing found a new direction. His first one-panel cartoon was published by Dragon Magazine in 1989. His path to the Dark Side was now paved in ink. He went on to have fairly regular cartoon appearances in the pages of Dragon. Turning to more comedic subjects, Aaron created a large-nosed henchman named Nodwick, gave him some of the most oddball adventurers to be employed by, and the rest is history. Nodwick continues to amuse and get maimed in the pages of Dragon Magazine, Dungeon Magazine, Nodwick Comics, and on Gamespy.com. He is also finding critical acclaim with his superhero-oriented comic book, ps238.

In spite of what his wife Cristi says, he still thinks he's funny.

REST INDEX PEACE

The following catalogues a handful of the many incidents where the henchman known as Nodwick either met his end, or soon would have if not for the ministrations of the legendary cleric, Piffany.

Entries followed by a "†" symbol reference pages in Volume I;
A "‡" symbol references pages in Volume II

DON'T FEAR THE REAPER

...and the hench-adventure continues...